BLETCHLEYPARK

CODEBREAKING PUZZLES

BLETCHLEYPARK

This edition was published in 2017 by the Bletchley Park Trust
The Mansion, Bletchley Park, Milton Keynes, MK3 6EB

ISBN: 978-1-78828-042-6
AD005832NT

Cover design by Rose
Printed in the UK

CONTENTS

INTRODUCTION

During World War Two, Bletchley Park was a workplace to thousands of people whose job it was to read the encrypted messages of its enemies. Towards the end of 1941, a crossword puzzle competition was organised by the *Daily Telegraph*. The challenge was to complete the puzzle in under 12 minutes. A Mr Gavin, Chairman of the Eccentrics Club, offered to donate £100 to the Minesweepers Fund, if it could be done under controlled conditions. As a number of the competitors were subsequently invited to take part in intelligence work at Bletchley Park, puzzles and codebreaking have been linked in the public mind ever since the exploits of Bletchley Park's Codebreakers became public knowledge.

Codebreaking is very much a puzzle-solving process and the codes and ciphers used are similar to the most common types of puzzles such as crosswords, wordsearches and sudoku. In many cases, the Codebreakers of Bletchley Park were looking for patterns in the problem before them, much like puzzle solvers today. Both often also base their solutions on clues. For example, a simple code might represent words by something else such as strings of numbers. In this case, the clue may lie in the frequency of certain strings of numbers occurring in the encrypted message. Straight or quick crossword clues are simple definitions of the answers, so the clue lies in the definition provided. A more difficult cipher might replace each letter in a message with another letter of the alphabet twice, a so-called double-encryption. This is a bit like cryptic crosswords in which the clues are puzzles in themselves.

Encrypted World War Two enemy messages were usually transmitted in groups of letters, typically 4 or 5 in length. So when the letters were decrypted, they would still be in these letter groups but some letters might be missing. The Codebreakers would then have to piece the actual words of the message together. This is a bit like a 'fill-in-the-blank' clue in crosswords or wordsearch puzzles.

So you see, puzzle solving is synonymous with the profound intellectual feat and remarkable brains of those whose work at Bletchley Park is said to have helped shorten World War Two by up to two years. Following in this long-held tradition, the Bletchley Park Trust has today produced this series of puzzle books so that you can follow in the footsteps of the Codebreakers and perhaps establish whether you have the puzzle-solving skills needed to have worked at wartime Bletchley Park...

1 The Spies and the Ministers

Six guests have arrived at Bletchley Park, and it is your job to escort them from reception to a holding room.

Due to security protocols, you are only able to escort a maximum of two guests at any one time. This means that you will have to make multiple journeys from reception to the briefing room.

The six guests consist of three spies and three ministers. It is an additional security requirement, however, that if there are both spies and ministers in a room that there can never be more spies than there are ministers. This applies to both the reception and the briefing room. For example if the briefing room already contains two ministers and one spy then you cannot escort two spies to the room, even if one were to then leave again with you, because there would (however briefly) be more spies than ministers in the room.

To make things more difficult, you are also required by social protocols to always have one guest with you at all times, even when returning from the briefing room back to reception.

Without dropping any guests off in other rooms, how can you transport all six guests from reception to the briefing room without breaking any of the security or social protocols?

Consonant Compression

2

All of the vowels, spaces and hyphens have been deleted from the following **members of the clergy**. Some extra spaces have then been inserted to help disguise the original text.

Can you restore the vowels, spacing and hyphens to reveal the original words?

PP LN NC

RC HBS HP

RVR ND

M NS TR

P STR

CNN

3

Code-breaking Challenge

Decode these sentences which have each had a letter-shift encryption applied. This is commonly known as a Caesar cipher.

Each letter in the alphabet has been replaced with a different letter that is a fixed number of places further down the alphabet, wrapping around from A to Z. For example, if P was changed to Y then Q would be changed to Z, and R would be changed to A.

The three cryptograms may or may not use the same letter shifts as one another.

Cz sio uly lyuxcha nbcm, nbyh sio'py mowwymmzoffs xywixyx cn

Ybckzsrus wg dcksf, obr wbtcfaohwcb wg zwpsfohwcb

Z Bzdrzq bhogdq gzr addm zookhdc sn sghr sdws

Character Camouflage

Delete one letter from each of the following pairs of letters so as to reveal the names of five **skiing terms**. For example, CD AE OT could be solved as C~~D~~ A~~E~~ ~~O~~T to reveal CAT.

ED NO WE ON HO RI EL LS

GR NO AG TG SL DE YS

PR OE SW ED LE RY

CF LR EO SE US TR YE LD EY

SP IH SA TZ ER

5 Initial Confusion

The initials of five **famous novels and their authors** are given below. By using your word skills and general knowledge, can you restore all of the original titles and authors?

T C I T R by J D S

A T O T C by C D

A A I W by L C

T D V C by D B

T A O S H by A C D

Fragmented Knowledge

6

Rearrange and join together the word fragments below in order to reveal five **feature-film genres**. All twenty of the fragments are sorted into alphabetical order – it is up to you to work out which fragment belongs to which genre.

ADV	AL	CE	DET
ECT	EN	ENT	FI
FIC	HIS	IC	IR
IVE	LM	NO	ON
SCI	TI	TOR	URE

7

Hidden Connections

Each of the following pairs of words secretly conceals a third word. This third word can be added to the end of the first word, and the start of the second word, to form two new words. Can you reveal all six hidden words? For example, GRID _____ SMITH is hiding the word LOCK, to make GRIDLOCK and LOCKSMITH.

PEA __________ EYED

BUMBLE __________ WAX

REIN __________ FULLY

OUT __________ TIER

QUICK __________ TONE

HEAD __________ FALLS

Cipher Decipher

8

Decode the names of five **baby animals** by cracking the Caesar cipher. Shift each letter a consistent amount forwards or backwards through the alphabet. For example, you might replace A with C, B with D, C with E and so on. The same code is used for every line.

WNVDEBGZ

EXOXKXM

DBMMXG

IBZEXM

VABVD

9

Mixed-up Messages

Each of the following six **bowling terms** have had their letters rearranged into alphabetical order. Can you unscramble them and restore all of the original words?

ABCGIKNSW

AFLT ABLL

AACDHINP

GIIKNNP

ABDORS

AEFMR

Digital Disguise

10

In the following mathematical sum, each digit has been disguised by replacing it with a different letter. None of the letters are equal to the same digit. Can you deduce the letter-to-number equivalence to reveal the original numerical sum? Some values are already given.

```
  GET
 +THE
 ----
  KEY
```

G=1   Y=5

11 Lost Letters

In all of the following **characters from Arthurian legend**, every other letter is missing. Can you restore the missing letters to reveal the original names?

L_D_ _F T_E L_K_

Q_E_N G_I_E_E_E

B_A_K K_I_H_

K_N_ _R_H_R

L_N_E_O_

M_R_R_D

The Clever Spy

12

An undercover spy was incarcerated in a secret prison, far from home. The guards at this prison were none too nice, and liked to play unpleasant games at the prisoners' expense.

One day, the guards told all of the prisoners that on the very next day they would stand all of the prisoners in a long line, each facing the back of the prisoner in front and unable to see any of the prisoners behind them. They would then start at the front of the line, with the prisoner who was unable to see any other prisoner, and place on their head either a green or a yellow cap. This would be done in such a way that the prisoner himself would be unable to see which of the two types of cap they were wearing.

The guards announced that they would then proceed up the line, giving each prisoner a cap, always either yellow or green, and always in such a way that the prisoner could not see which cap they were given, until they reached the end of the line. At this point they would then ask the prisoner at the end of the line, who had been able to see every cap other than his own, which cap *he* was wearing. If he answered correctly, he would be returned to his cell. If he answered incorrectly, he would have twenty-five years added to his sentence.

They would then proceed back up the line, prisoner-by-prisoner, until they reached the front of the line where the prisoner who had not seen any caps was standing. They would ask each prisoner in turn the same question, and they would carry out the same punishment for anyone answering incorrectly.

The guards also made it clear that the prisoners would not be able to communicate with each other in any way during the ordeal. They could do one thing and one thing only – call out 'green', or call out 'yellow'. They would, however, be allowed the evening to discuss any tactics they would want to employ on the following day to minimize the number of those who would be punished.

As soon as the guards had finished explaining the game, the undercover spy gathered all of the prisoners together and presented a plan to them. This plan would *guarantee* that either *all* of them or *all but one* of them would escape the twenty-five year additional sentence.

What was his plan, and how would it work?

13 Consonant Compression

All of the vowels, spaces and hyphens have been deleted from the following **Disney animated features**. Some extra spaces have then been inserted to help disguise the original text.

Can you restore the vowels, spacing and hyphens to reveal the original titles?

THH NC HB CKF NT RDM

T HPR NC SSND THF RG

B TYN DTHB ST

LD YND THT RMP

LLN DST TCH

P TRP N

Code-breaking Challenge

14

Decode these proverbs which have each had a particular encryption applied to them.

Each sentence uses the same encryption, and you will be able to crack this encryption without having any existing code-breaking skills!

Hgual dna eht dlrow shgual htiw uoy

Eht foorp fo eht gniddup si ni eht gnitae

Owt sgnorw t'nod ekam a thgir

15 Character Camouflage

Delete one letter from each of the following pairs of letters so as to reveal the names of five **electronic gadgets**. For example, CD AE OT could be solved as C~~D~~ A~~E~~ ~~O~~T to reveal CAT.

SP RP AI NI NT DE RY

TL RA PI TN OT PS

BS CL AO GN DN OE RN

TR AE BA LN ED TS

DC AR MO EN RL AD

Initial Confusion

16

The initials of five **famous children's books and their authors** are given below. By using your word skills and general knowledge, can you restore all of the original titles and authors?

T H by J R R T

H P A T C O S by J K R

T L T W A T W by C S L

B B by A S

C W by E B W

17 Fragmented Knowledge

Rearrange and join together the word fragments below in order to reveal five **parts of a ship**. All sixteen of the fragments are sorted into alphabetical order – it is up to you to work out which fragment belongs to which item.

ECA	FOR	IL	KER
LE	LE	LER	MAI
NNA	NSA	PEL	POR
PRO	SPI	ST	THO

Hidden Connections

18

Each of the following pairs of words secretly conceals a third word. This third word can be added to the end of the first word, and the start of the second word, to form two new words. Can you reveal all six hidden words? For example, GRID ____ SMITH is hiding the word LOCK, to make GRIDLOCK and LOCKSMITH.

BED __________ LINE

LIVE __________ PILED

GRAM __________ RED

BREAK __________ OUT

DOWN __________ TILE

WIRE __________ PING

19 Cipher Decipher

Decode the names of five **marsupial animals** by cracking the Caesar cipher. Shift each letter a consistent amount forwards or backwards through the alphabet. For example, you might replace A with C, B with D, C with E and so on. The same code is used for every line.

JQICQDYQD TULYB

JHUU AQDWQHEE

HESA MQBBQRO

RQDTYSEEJ

MECRQJ

Mixed-up Messages

Each of the following six **words connected with singing** have had their letters rearranged into alphabetical order. Can you unscramble them and restore all of the original words?

ADEEENRS

ACEILOVZ

ACINNT

ABELRW

DELOY

AAIR

21 Digital Disguise

In the following mathematical sum, each digit has been disguised by replacing it with a different letter. None of the letters are equal to the same digit. Can you deduce the letter-to-number equivalence to reveal the original numerical sum? Some values are already given.

```
  CODE
 +WORD
 -----
 CLOAK
```

K=3   D=7

Lost Letters

In all of the following **types of feature-film stunt**, every other letter is missing. Can you restore the missing letters to reveal the original words?

M_T_R_Y_L_ _E_P

S_O_D F_G_T

R_P_ _W_N_

B_S_ _U_P

C_R C_A_E

S_Y_I_E

23 The Exceptional Agent

A certain international agent was hosting an annual dinner for intelligence colleagues and their partners, where only the brightest and the best were invited. Along with his own partner, there would be just four other couples attending, for a total of ten people at the dinner.

After all four visiting couples had arrived and had been seated, each individual was asked to provide a card containing details of their assumed identity to every other person in the room who they had not met prior to arriving.

The hosting agent then observed that all eight members of the four couples attending had received a different number of identity cards to all of the others, and that furthermore he himself had also received a different number again.

Now, using your own deductive powers, work out how many identity cards *the hosting agent's partner* had received.

Consonant Compression

24

All of the vowels, spaces and hyphens have been deleted from the following **parts of a castle**. Some extra spaces have then been inserted to help disguise the original text.

Can you restore the vowels, spacing and hyphens to reveal the original words?

BT TLM NTS

L KTW R

DR WB RDG

PR TC LLS

G THS

D NG N

25 Code-breaking Challenge

Decode these proverbs which have each had a particular encryption applied to them.

Each sentence uses the same encryption, and you should be able to crack this encryption without having any existing code-breaking skills!

Hwret eehers' umkc htre'eb sarss

Ohem si hwret eeh ehrai ts

Htd eveli si ni htd eteiasl

Character Camouflage

26

Delete one letter from each of the following pairs of letters so as to reveal the names of five **large countries**. For example, CD AE OT could be solved as C~~D~~ A~~E~~ ~~O~~T to reveal CAT.

NA IU SC AT RT AE LG IK AE

PM EO LX IA CR OD

FR UR SA NS KI AE

TB AR AI WZ IE LM

CB RA NI AT DA NA

27 Initial Confusion

The initials of five **IMDB top-rated feature films** are given below. By using your word skills and general knowledge, can you restore all of the original titles?

TLOTRTROTK

SWEVTESB

OFOTCN

DSOHILTSWALTB

ESOTSM

Fragmented Knowledge

Rearrange and join together the word fragments below in order to reveal five **types of dance**. All 22 of the fragments are sorted into alphabetical order – it is up to you to work out which fragment belongs to which dance.

AND BE BOS CHA

CK DOB LAM LE

LK LL NO ON

PA RLE RO RO

SA SO ST TH

VA WA

29 Hidden Connections

Each of the following pairs of words secretly conceals a third word. This third word can be added to the end of the first word, and the start of the second word, to form two new words. Can you reveal all six hidden words? For example, GRID ____ SMITH is hiding the word LOCK, to make GRIDLOCK and LOCKSMITH.

OUT __________ ALIKE

SAND __________ WEIGHT

GUN __________ LESS

WIND __________ BOARD

SCARE __________ BARS

HAND __________ DOWN

Cipher Decipher

Decode the names of five **shades of yellow** by cracking the Caesar cipher. Shift each letter a consistent amount forwards or backwards through the alphabet. For example, you might replace A with C, B with D, C with E and so on. The same code is used for every line.

VSXXGVAD

WYYKZWDD

ESYFGDAS

HJAEJGKW

EMKLSJV

31 Mixed-up Messages

Each of the following six **physics terms** have had their letters rearranged into alphabetical order. Can you unscramble them and restore all of the original words?

ADGNR DEFIINU EHORTY

ACEFGILNRTU CEFOR

AMNQTUU ACCEHIMNS

AEILNOPTT EEGNRY

ACHIN ACEINORT

ACDEHIMMNORSTY

Digital Disguise

In the following mathematical sum, each digit has been disguised by replacing it with a different letter. None of the letters are equal to the same digit. Can you deduce the letter-to-number equivalence to reveal the original numerical sum? Some values are already given.

```
 SHIFT
+ONLY
------
 NOTES
```

O=4   L=8

33 Lost Letters

In all of the following **pieces of climbing equipment**, every other letter is missing. Can you restore the missing letters to reveal the original words?

B_L_Y D_V_C_

C_R_B_N_R

D_S_E_D_R

H_R_E_S

H_L_E_

P_T_N_

The Odds of Survival

The life of a spy is inherently dangerous, but there are often chances to minimize the risks.

One particularly reckless international agent one day found himself on the set of a bizarre television game show, where the prize was not a washing machine or pile of cash but rather the chance to survive.

He was given a challenge, and told that if he answered correctly he would survive – but if he answered incorrectly he would never leave the studio alive.

The spy was presented with three doors. One of the doors had nothing behind it, but the other two had armed assassins standing ready and waiting behind them. The spy had no idea which was which, and would simply have to guess.

The host of this strange televisual event asked the spy which door he wished to open. With seemingly casual indifference, the spy made his choice, and the host went over as if to open it. But before he did, he stopped and spoke to the spy:

"You have chosen this door. That means there are *two* doors you did *not* choose, one of which has an assassin behind. We will not be needing him today, so I will open his door and allow him to come out and watch you receive your fate."

The host then opened one of the two doors that had not been chosen, and allowed the waiting assassin to step out into the studio. The host then continued:

"However, I also offer you a choice. You have selected this door that remains unopened, but there is now also one other door that is unopened. You may, if you wish, switch your guess to this other unopened door. Do you wish to do so, or do you want to stick with your original choice?"

Which door should the spy choose? Should they switch, stick with their original choice, or does it not matter?

35 Consonant Compression

All of the vowels, spaces and hyphens have been deleted from the following **Sherlock Holmes characters**. Some extra spaces have then been inserted to help disguise the original text.

Can you restore the vowels, spacing and hyphens to reveal the original names?

MR SH DSN

RND LR

L ST RD

MR RTY

W TSN

MR Y

Code-breaking Challenge

Decode these proverbs which have each had a particular encryption applied to them.

Each sentence uses the same encryption, and you will be able to crack this encryption without having any existing code-breaking skills!

Cover real images – mostly extreme darkness obscures every small, nice thing placed artistically, y'all

Bring lots of oval diamonds with inclusive lots loaded to every linked lozenge

Mostly one needs every yarn in stereo placement, or words easily recede

37 Character Camouflage

Delete one letter from each of the following pairs of letters so as to reveal the names of five **types of musician**. For example, CD AE OT could be solved as C~~D~~ A~~E~~ ~~O~~T to reveal CAT.

BT RE UA TM PB EO WT DE YR

PV EI OA NL IE NT IA SL YT

PD RL AU MY EM ER TR

DC EO MN DP OU CS ET RO RT

TS OE PN RO RA SN OD

Initial Confusion

The initials of five **plays by Shakespeare** are given below. By using your word skills and general knowledge, can you restore all of the original titles?

AWTEW

AYLI

LLL

TGOV

MND

39 Fragmented Knowledge

Rearrange and join together the word fragments below in order to reveal five **economics terms**. All twenty of the fragments are sorted into alphabetical order – it is up to you to work out which fragment belongs to which term.

AL	BUT	COL	CON
DIS	EMP	ER	EST
INV	ION	LAT	LOY
ME	ME	NT	NT
ON	PTI	SUM	TRI

Hidden Connections

Each of the following pairs of words secretly conceals a third word. This third word can be added to the end of the first word, and the start of the second word, to form two new words. Can you reveal all six hidden words? For example, GRID _____ SMITH is hiding the word LOCK, to make GRIDLOCK and LOCKSMITH.

CON __________ WARE

OVER __________ SOME

CHEST __________ HELLS

HERE __________ KING

COUNTER __________ POSTING

MAN __________ BAR

41 Cipher Decipher

Decode the names of five **things associated with vampire mythology** by cracking the Caesar cipher. Shift each letter a consistent amount forwards or backwards through the alphabet. For example, you might replace A with C, B with D, C with E and so on. The same code is used for every line.

VTCPUANXCPKC

JQNA YCVGT

ICTNKE

OKTTQTU

UKNXGT

Mixed-up Messages

Each of the following six **teaching staff** have had their letters rearranged into alphabetical order. Can you unscramble them and restore all of the original words?

AADEEHMRST

AAINSSSTT

ACIILNPPR

EFOOPRRSS

CEELRRTU

ORTTU

43 Digital Disguise

In the following mathematical sum, each digit has been disguised by replacing it with a different letter. None of the letters are equal to the same digit. Can you deduce the letter-to-number equivalence to reveal the original numerical sum?

```
  CHANGE
+CODING
-------
RECODED
```

Lost Letters

44

In all of the following **types of aircraft**, every other letter is missing. Can you restore the missing letters to reveal the original words?

H_L_C_P_E_

A_U_P_A_E

T_R_O_R_P

J_M_O _E_

Z_P_E_I_

G_I_E_

45 The Potential Traitors

Seven potentially rogue spies have been arrested under suspicion of being members of a traitorous circle, and are being questioned by an investigatory panel.

The seven spies stand in line in front of the panel and then each speaks in turn:

Spy A: Exactly one spy is lying

Spy B: Exactly two spies are lying

Spy C: Exactly three spies are lying

Spy D: Exactly four spies are lying

Spy E: Exactly five spies are lying

Spy F: Exactly six spies are lying

Spy G: All seven of us are lying

What can the investigatory panel conclude? How many of these spies, A to G, have told you the truth?

Consonant Compression

All of the vowels, spaces and hyphens have been deleted from the following **IMDB top-rated feature films**. Some extra spaces have then been inserted to help disguise the original text.

Can you restore the vowels, spacing and hyphens to reveal the original titles?

THG DT HBDN DT HG LY

RD RSF THL STRK

THS LSSP CTS

L FSB TFL

PCL YP SNW

MM NT

47 Code-breaking Challenge

Decode these proverbs which have each had a particular encryption applied to them.

Each sentence uses the same encryption, and you will not require any existing code-breaking skills, or any external references, to crack this code.

2 5 1 21 20 25 9 19 9 14
20 8 5 5 25 5 15 6 20 8 5
2 5 8 15 12 4 5 18

1 12 12 20 8 1 20
7 12 9 20 20 5 18 19 9 19
14 15 20 7 15 12 4

7 9 22 5 3 18 5 4 9 20
23 8 5 18 5 3 18 5 4 9 20
9 19 4 21 5

Character Camouflage 48

Delete one letter from each of the following pairs of letters so as to reveal the names of five **tennis terms**. For example, CD AE OT could be solved as C~~D~~ A~~E~~ ~~O~~T to reveal CAT.

SB AP IC NK SH AH EN LD

WA DI NV AN NE RT YA GA EY

LD OE SU BE LR NE SO

BS OE RU NV CI CE EN

UR MU LP IE DR EN

49 Initial Confusion

The initials of the titles of five **books by Charles Dickens** are given below. By using your word skills and general knowledge, can you restore all of the original titles?

D C

T O C S

N N

O T

T P P

Fragmented Knowledge

50

Rearrange and join together the word fragments below in order to reveal five **condiments**. All eighteen of the fragments are sorted into alphabetical order – it is up to you to work out which fragment belongs to which condiment.

ADE ADI BUT CON

HOR JEL LY MAL

MAR MI NT NUT

PEA SER SER SH

TER VE

51 Hidden Connections

Each of the following pairs of words secretly conceals a third word. This third word can be added to the end of the first word, and the start of the second word, to form two new words. Can you reveal all six hidden words? For example, GRID _____ SMITH is hiding the word LOCK, to make GRIDLOCK and LOCKSMITH.

MAKE __________ HOT

HOUSE __________ OVER

HOME __________ HIP

VIE __________ PANS

FARM __________ TICKS

NOSE __________ STING

Cipher Decipher

Decode the names of five **internal computer components** by cracking the Caesar cipher. Shift each letter a consistent amount forwards or backwards through the alphabet. For example, you might replace A with C, B with D, C with E and so on. The same code is used for every line.

EOXHWRRWK FDUG

KDUG GULYH

VRXQG FDUG

KHDW VLQN

SURFHVVRU

53

Mixed-up Messages

Each of the following six **superhero powers** have had their letters rearranged into alphabetical order. Can you unscramble them and restore all of the original words?

AGIRTVY AAIILMNNOPTU

CCEEILOPST IINOSV

ABEIIILLNNRTUVY

EPRSU EGHNRSTT

BIIIIILNSTVY

BEW GGIILNNS

Digital Disguise

In the following mathematical sum, each digit has been disguised by replacing it with a different letter. None of the letters are equal to the same digit. Can you deduce the letter-to-number equivalence to reveal the original numerical sum? Some values are already given.

```
 HIDE
 +THE
+CODE
-----
COVER
```

T=3 R=6 I=9

55 Lost Letters

In all of the following **things you might find under the sea**, every other letter is missing. Can you restore the missing letters to reveal the original words?

S_I_W_E_K

B_R_A_L_

S_A_O_S_

D_L_H_N

O_T_P_S

C_R_L

Spy Gadgets

56

Four UK-based spies are on location in four different places to intercept potential security threats. Each has one of four different gadgets to help them. Can you work out which spy is in what place, with what gadget – and what technology each gadget is based on.

1. James was on location in Bletchley Park.
2. The Vocalitass was not needed at a UK location, but was powered by Quantum Listening.
3. The spy whose device was powered by Inverse Phasing was at the UK Parliament, but he did not use the Craniator.
4. Jimmy Blond did not visit The White House, but he did leave the UK.
5. The Viral Attachment technology was used by the spy who had the Netterbot, which was neither James or Jimmy.

		Gadget				Location				Technology			
		Interceptorion	Craniator	Vocalitass	Netterbot	UK Parliament	Bletchley Park, UK	The White House	CIA Headquarters	Inverse Phasing	Quantum Listening	Latent Observation	Viral Attachment
Spy	Jimmy Blond												
	James Welsh												
	Richard Cord												
	Karen Ambler												
Technology	Inverse Phasing												
	Quantum Listening												
	Latent Observation												
	Viral Attachment												
Location	UK Parliament												
	Bletchley Park, UK												
	The White House												
	CIA Headquarters												

Spy	Location	Gadget	Technology

57 Consonant Compression

All of the vowels, spaces and hyphens have been deleted from the following **legendary characters**. Some extra spaces have then been inserted to help disguise the original text.

Can you restore the vowels, spacing and hyphens to reveal the original names?

PR SS

RB NHD

GL GM SH

CH LLS

L NC LT

M DS

Code-breaking Challenge

Decode these proverbs which have each had a particular encryption applied to them.

Each sentence uses the same encryption, and you should be able to crack this encryption without having any existing code-breaking skills!

But Sierra call elk – pastrami has chic cash – ace bandana leap

What alkali sham! We sow broccoli until all hast gone full haul

Past your impromptu act with callow libretti, shrill wail – so you want

59 Character Camouflage

Delete one letter from each of the following pairs of letters so as to reveal the names of five **large animals**. For example, CD AE OT could be solved as C~~D~~ A~~E~~ ~~O~~T to reveal CAT.

CE LR EO CP HO AY EN TD

MG OA NR KI LO DL EA

SP OU RP EC UR PC IO NA EY

SW PH AO LR DE

AS NQ OU IW BR OR EA PL

Initial Confusion

The initials of five **hit songs by the Beatles** are given below. By using your word skills and general knowledge, can you restore all of the original titles?

A Y N I L

C B M L

A H D N

H J

I W T H Y H

61 Fragmented Knowledge

Rearrange and join together the word fragments below in order to reveal five **words and phrases associated with the Old West**. All eighteen of the fragments are sorted into alphabetical order – it is up to you to work out which fragment belongs to which item.

BAG BLA BST CKS

DLE ER GH GUN

HI MI NG NO

ON ONE SAD SLI

TH TOM

Hidden Connections

Each of the following pairs of words secretly conceals a third word. This third word can be added to the end of the first word, and the start of the second word, to form two new words. Can you reveal all six hidden words? For example, GRID _____ SMITH is hiding the word LOCK, to make GRIDLOCK and LOCKSMITH.

DIE __________ BACK

GIRL __________ HIP

EAR __________ TIC

LIT __________ HOW

BED __________ HANDLERS

LIFT __________ HOOTS

63

Cipher Decipher

Decode the names of five **construction-site machines** by cracking the Caesar cipher. Shift each letter a consistent amount forwards or backwards through the alphabet. For example, you might replace A with C, B with D, C with E and so on. The same code is used for every line.

MFIB AOFSBO

YRIIALWBO

BUZXSXQLO

YXZHELB

DOXABO

Mixed-up Messages

Each of the following six **classic arcade games** have had their letters rearranged into alphabetical order. Can you unscramble them and restore all of the original titles?

DEKNOY GKNO IJNORU

EIILMSS ACDMMNO

ACEPS ADEINRSV

ELOP IINOOPST

ADEIORSST

CDEEEINPT

65 Digital Disguise

In the following mathematical sum, each digit has been disguised by replacing it with a different letter. None of the letters are equal to the same digit. Can you deduce the letter-to-number equivalence to reveal the original numerical sum? Some values are already given.

```
 SPOT
 -THE
-MOLE
-----
  NOW
```

O=3 W=5

E=6 H=8

Lost Letters

In all of the following **words of Germanic origin**, every other letter is missing. Can you restore the missing letters to reveal the original words?

D_P_E_G_N_E_

K_N_E_G_R_E_

F_A_K_U_T_R

P_L_E_G_I_T

W_N_E_L_S_

S_R_D_L

67 The Spy Show Finale

Having survived the main part of a strange, dystopian television game show (see page 39), the spy is introduced to the final round. Bound and gagged, he is unable to do anything other than mutely observe proceedings.

In this round his odds are reduced to one in two. He is shown an empty box, along with two pieces of paper. On one piece of paper the word 'WIN' has been written, and on the other is the word 'LOSE'. The papers are folded and placed into the box, and the spy is told that he will shortly be asked to draw one out of the box at random. If he chooses 'WIN', he will be spared – but if he chooses 'LOSE', his life will be forfeit.

The spy has resigned himself to his 50:50 fate, when, to his surprise, the television show goes to a commercial break for full dramatic effect. All of the staff leave the set. The only remaining person is one of the assassins who was not given the opportunity to kill him earlier.

Seeking his revenge, the assassin laughs at the spy and shows him a third piece of paper, this one also with 'LOSE' written on it. He then goes over to the box, finds the paper with 'WIN' written on it and removes it, replacing it with the piece of paper which has 'LOSE' on it. There are now two 'LOSE's and no 'WIN's in the box.

The staff return to the set, and the spy is freed from his bindings and ungagged. The spy does not, however, seek to explain about the duplicate 'LOSE', for he has a plan that he believes will guarantee his survival.

What is his plan?

Consonant Compression

All of the vowels, spaces and hyphens have been deleted from the following **types of boat**. Some extra spaces have then been inserted to help disguise the original text.

Can you restore the vowels, spacing and hyphens to reveal the original words and phrases?

RC RF TCR RR

SPRT NKR

M NSW PR

PD DLS TMR

L FB T

DR DG R

69 Code-breaking Challenge

Decode these proverbs which have each had a particular encryption applied to them.

Each sentence uses the same encryption, and you will not require any existing code-breaking skills to crack this code.

00101 10110 00101 10010 11001
00011 01100 01111 10101 00100
01000 00001 10011
00001
10011 01001 01100 10110 00101 10010
01100 01001 01110 01001 01110 00111

00010 00101 10100 10100 00101 10010
10011 00001 00110 00101
10100 01000 00001 01110
10011 01111 10010 10010 11001

01101 01111 10010 00101
01000 00001 10011 10100 00101
01100 00101 10011 10011
10011 10000 00101 00101 00100

Character Camouflage 70

Delete one letter from each of the following pairs of letters so as to reveal the names of five **tools**. For example, CD AE OT could be solved as C~~D~~ A~~E~~ ~~O~~T to reveal CAT.

DC HR AO PI SN ES DA LW

WH AH MA CM KE RS

BP LO EA TN ER

TS UC RT NE YW DT HR IO VN EG TR

YW RA NE KN LC HY

71

Initial Confusion

The initials of five **Best Actor Oscar winners and the feature films for which they won** are given below. By using your word skills and general knowledge, can you restore all of the original names?

C F for T K S

E R for T T O E

L D for T R

K S for A B

T H for F G

Fragmented Knowledge

Rearrange and join together the word fragments below in order to reveal five **basketball terms**. All eighteen of the fragments are sorted into alphabetical order – it is up to you to work out which fragment belongs to which term.

ARD BAC BAC BOU

EE FR KBO KCO

NDS OF ON OUT

OW POS SES SI

THR URT

73

Hidden Connections

Each of the following pairs of words secretly conceals a third word. This third word can be added to the end of the first word, and the start of the second word, to form two new words. Can you reveal all six hidden words? For example, GRID _____ SMITH is hiding the word LOCK, to make GRIDLOCK and LOCKSMITH.

SOUTH __________ WARD

GRAND __________ DIES

CON __________ ABLE

DIS __________ ION

OVER __________ ABLE

FINGER __________ OUT

Cipher Decipher

Decode the names of five **types of diet** by cracking the Caesar cipher. Shift each letter a consistent amount forwards or backwards through the alphabet. For example, you might replace A with C, B with D, C with E and so on. The same code is used for every line.

BTSXITGGPCTPC

WXVW-EGDITXC

VAJITC-UGTT

EPATDAXIWXR

ETHRPIPGXPC

75 Mixed-up Messages

Each of the following six **seabirds** have had their letters rearranged into alphabetical order. Can you unscramble them and restore all of the original words?

ACCEEHORRSTTY

AAEEHRRSTW

AABLORSST

ACMNOORRT

EGILLMOTU

EGINNPU

Digital Disguise

In the following mathematical sum, each digit has been disguised by replacing it with a different letter. None of the letters are equal to the same digit. Can you deduce the letter-to-number equivalence to reveal the original numerical sum? Some values are already given.

```
  ADD
+THE
+SUM
----
 THIS
```

E=0 H=5 S=6

77 Lost Letters

In all of the following **three-dimensional solids**, every other letter is missing. Can you restore the missing letters to reveal the original words?

D_D_C_H_D_O_

C_L_N_E_

P_R_M_D

C_B_I_

S_H_R_

T_R_S

Ammunition Boxes

A disorganized spy has stored all of his ammunition in three boxes, each containing a label as to what is inside.

One box has 'pistol ammunition' written on it, while another has 'rifle ammunition'. A third simply says 'mixed pistol and rifle ammunition', indicating that it includes at least one item of pistol ammunition and at least one item of rifle ammunition.

The spy remembers that every box has the wrong label on it, but he realizes that all he needs to do is take one single item from one single box, without looking at either the rest of its contents or any of the other boxes, in order to be certain what each box contains.

Can you explain how the spy is able to do this?

79 Consonant Compression

All of the vowels, spaces and hyphens have been deleted from the following **hot drinks**. Some extra spaces have then been inserted to help disguise the original text.

Can you restore the vowels, spacing and hyphens to reveal the original drinks?

MLLD WN

CPPCCN

SPRSS

MRCN

GGNG

SK

Code-breaking Challenge

Decode these proverbs which have each had a particular encryption applied to them.

Each sentence uses the same encryption, and in order to be able to crack this code it will help to have solved one of the 'Cipher Decipher' puzzles, or the 'Code-breaking Challenge' on page 8.

DOG: Osz wvk eiehf hhkgus

CAT: Kt bu bxvtxt th iiog tacn mq rxeebxe

PIGLET: Lpge chj luy'x dcwc neg'i pacx rdc

81 Character Camouflage

Delete one letter from each of the following pairs of letters so as to reveal the names of five **Olympic sports**. For example, CD AE OT could be solved as C~~D~~ A~~E~~ ~~O~~T to reveal CAT.

DS WR EI MA NM EI RN GS

FB AE AD MT HI EN RT SO NY

SV UO LC CL EA YD BT IA NL GL

GF LY YM IN GA TS HT AI CN GS

SA RH CO HO TE YR YS

Initial Confusion

The initials of five **Best Actress Oscar winners and the feature films for which they won** are given below. By using your word skills and general knowledge, can you restore all of the original names?

E S for L L L

J M for S A

J L for S L P

N P for B S

K W for T R

83 Fragmented Knowledge

Rearrange and join together the word fragments below in order to reveal five **theatrical terms**. All 22 of the fragments are sorted into alphabetical order – it is up to you to work out which fragment belongs to which term.

AG CA CUR ER

FIR FRI GE GE

GHT HES HT IN

LL MAN NIG ORC

PIT ST STA STA

TA TRA

Hidden Connections

84

Each of the following pairs of words secretly conceals a third word. This third word can be added to the end of the first word, and the start of the second word, to form two new words. Can you reveal all six hidden words? For example, GRID _____ SMITH is hiding the word LOCK, to make GRIDLOCK and LOCKSMITH.

OUT __________ DIES

COCK __________ TING

DOWN __________ OUT

LIGHT __________ LESS

HENCE __________ WITH

OVER __________ ABLE

85 Cipher Decipher

Decode the names of five **moons of Saturn** by cracking the Caesar cipher. Shift each letter a consistent amount forwards or backwards through the alphabet. For example, you might replace A with C, B with D, C with E and so on. The same code is used for every line.

KMJHZOCZPN

CTKZMDJI

XVGTKNJ

DVKZOPN

ODOVI

Mixed-up Messages

Each of the following six **spacecraft** have had their letters rearranged into alphabetical order. Can you unscramble them and restore all of the original names?

AMRS ADEFHINPRT

ALNRU BEIORRT

ACEPS EHLSTTU

EEEGMNRSS

AEGILLO

IKNPSTU

87

Digital Disguise

In the following mathematical sum, each digit has been disguised by replacing it with a different letter. None of the letters are equal to the same digit. Can you deduce the letter-to-number equivalence to reveal the original numerical sum? One value is already given.

$$\begin{array}{r} \text{GOT} \\ \times\,\text{THE} \\ \hline \text{CODES} \end{array}$$

E=8

Lost Letters

In all of the following **fencing terms**, every other letter is missing. Can you restore the missing letters to reveal the original terms?

E_ _A_D_

R_P_S_E

A_T_C_

P_M_E_

F_I_T

L_N_E

89 The Confounded Spy

A clever spy once found himself the captive of a well-known, but slightly crazy, billionaire. The billionaire considered himself something of an evil mastermind, and so decided to challenge the spy to a duel of wits.

First, he gave the spy this challenge:

1. I have two henchmen. One of them I have instructed to always tell the truth, no matter what. The other I have instructed to always lie, no matter what.

   I will give you one question, to ask to one of the henchmen of your choice. If, after that question, you can successfully tell me which of the henchmen I told to always tell the truth, and which I told to always lie, then I shall free you.

The spy thought about this challenge, and then found the perfect question. What did he ask, to guarantee that he would correctly identify each henchman?

After the spy had correctly identified the henchmen, the billionaire revealed, with what he thought was a suitably evil laugh, that he had lied, and there was a further challenge the spy would have to pass:

2. I have now hired three more henchman, and instructed one to always lie, one to always tell the truth, and the third to answer as he pleases – he may either lie or tell the truth.

   One of the three henchmen now says to you, 'I always lie'. If you can tell me which of the three henchmen this was – the truth-teller, the liar, or the one who may do either – then I will set you free. And I really will, this time.

The spy proceeded to answer correctly, and was at last duly freed. What was his answer?

Consonant Compression

All of the vowels, spaces and hyphens have been deleted from the following **water sports**. Some extra spaces have then been inserted to help disguise the original text.

Can you restore the vowels, spacing and hyphens to reveal the original words and phrases?

SY NCH RNZ DD VNG

B DYB RD NG

K TS RF NG

W TR PL

K YK NG

F SHN G

91 Code-breaking Challenge

Decode these proverbs which have each had a particular encryption applied to them.

Each sentence uses the same encryption, and you will not require any existing code-breaking skills to crack this code.

14 08 05
04 05 16 09 0C
09 13
09 0E
14 08 05
04 05 14 01 09 0C 13

03 08 01 12 09 14 19
02 05 07 09 0E 13
01 14
08 0F 0D 05

19 0F 15 12 05
0E 05 16 05 12
14 0F 0F
0F 0C 04
14 0F
0C 05 01 12 0E

Character Camouflage

92

Delete one letter from each of the following pairs of letters so as to reveal the names of five **US states**. For example, CD AE OT could be solved as C~~D~~ A~~E~~ ~~O~~T to reveal CAT.

FG EL OE RT IG IN EA

NM IE BC HR IA SG TA AN

KO AR EN SG EO NR

MV IA TR HG LI NA NI AD

AW LY OA BP IA MN AG

93 Initial Confusion

The initials of five of the **longest-running Broadway musicals** are given below. By using your word skills and general knowledge, can you restore all of the original titles?

TPOTO

BATB

TBOM

FOTR

TLK

Fragmented Knowledge

Rearrange and join together the word fragments below in order to reveal five **superhero characters**. All 24 of the fragments are sorted into alphabetical order – it is up to you to work out which fragment belongs to which character.

AME	AN	AN	BLE
CA	CAP	DER	EN
FAN	GRE	IN	INV
ISI	LAN	MR	RI
RN	TA	TAS	TE
TIC	WOM	WOM	WON

95 Hidden Connections

Each of the following pairs of words secretly conceals a third word. This third word can be added to the end of the first word, and the start of the second word, to form two new words. Can you reveal all six hidden words? For example, GRID _____ SMITH is hiding the word LOCK, to make GRIDLOCK and LOCKSMITH.

BATH __________ MATES

INTERNS __________ PIES

HOMES __________ TING

MAR __________ FOIL

ONE __________ LESS

BLUE __________ LAND

Cipher Decipher

Decode the names of five **Impressionist painters** by cracking the Caesar cipher. Shift each letter a consistent amount forwards or backwards through the alphabet. For example, you might replace A with C, B with D, C with E and so on. The same code is used for every line.

DTCESWGOQPF

RKUUCTTQ

EGBCPPG

TGPQKT

OQPGV

97 Mixed-up Messages

Each of the following six **types of seat** have had their letters rearranged into alphabetical order. Can you unscramble them and restore all of the original words?

ACEHIS EGLNOU

CEEJORT

AMNOOTT

ADDELS

BCEHN

ADINV

Digital Disguise

In the following mathematical sum, each digit has been disguised by replacing it with a different letter. None of the letters are equal to the same digit. Can you deduce the letter-to-number equivalence to reveal the original numerical sum?

```
   THIS
  ×THAT
-------
RESULTS
```

99

Lost Letters

In all of the following **items of neckwear**, every other letter is missing. Can you restore the missing letters to reveal the original words?

N_C_E_C_I_F

B_W T_E

M_F_L_R

C_A_A_

S_A_F

S_O_E

Hidden Connections

Each of the following pairs of words secretly conceals a third word. This third word can be added to the end of the first word, and the start of the second word, to form two new words. Can you reveal all six hidden words? For example, GRID _____ SMITH is hiding the word LOCK, to make GRIDLOCK and LOCKSMITH.

POST __________ BOARD

UNDER __________ LOAD

AIR __________ MEN

PAS __________ FISHES

MINE __________ WORK

TIME __________ CLOTH

101 Consonant Compression

All of the vowels, spaces and hyphens have been deleted from the following **large islands**. Some extra spaces have then been inserted to help disguise the original text.

Can you restore the vowels, spacing and hyphens to reveal the original names?

N WF NDL ND

GR TBR TN

MD GS CR

S MTR

N WGN

C B

Fragmented Knowledge

Rearrange and join together the word fragments below in order to reveal five **elements of the Periodic Table**. All sixteen of the fragments are sorted into alphabetical order – it is up to you to work out which fragment belongs to which element.

BER	ESE	GAN	GER
IUM	IUM	IUM	MAG
MAN	MAN	NES	OR
PHO	SPH	US	YLL

103 Mixed-up Messages

Each of the following six **types of alarm signal** have had their letters rearranged into alphabetical order. Can you unscramble them and restore all of the original words?

HOST ACORSS EHT BOSW

AFGHILNS GHILT

CEILOP EHILSTW

MORST AGINNRW

ACR HNOR

DER AFGL

Cipher Decipher

Decode the names of five **mathematical terms** by cracking the Caesar cipher. Shift each letter a consistent amount forwards or backwards through the alphabet. For example, you might replace A with C, B with D, C with E and so on. The same code is used for every line.

UCTBQXTQKIBQWV

IZQBPUMBQK

TWOIZQBPU

VCUMZIBWZ

MYCIBQWV

105 Lost Letters

In all of the following **things associated with laundry**, every other letter is missing. Can you restore the missing letters to reveal the original words?

F_B_I_ _O_T_N_R

W_S_I_G P_W_E_

D_Y C_E_N_N_

T_M_L_ _R_E_

D_Y_N_ _A_K

S_E_M _R_N

Hidden Connections

Each of the following pairs of words secretly conceals a third word. This third word can be added to the end of the first word, and the start of the second word, to form two new words. Can you reveal all six hidden words? For example, GRID _____ SMITH is hiding the word LOCK, to make GRIDLOCK and LOCKSMITH.

FUN __________ LOPED

RING __________ HIP

WAVE __________ WISE

SHORT __________ TINGS

TURN __________ ROOM

HAY __________ TAPPING

107 Digital Disguise

In the following mathematical sum, each digit has been disguised by replacing it with a different letter. None of the letters are equal to the same digit. Can you deduce the letter-to-number equivalence to reveal the original numerical sum? Some values are already given.

```
 THINK
+HARD
------
 TRUTH
```

H=1 D=7 A=8

Code-breaking Challenge

Decode these proverbs which have each had a particular encryption applied to them.

Each sentence uses the same encryption, and you will not require any existing code-breaking skills, or any external references, to crack this code.

Po epph effe tfph efitjovqov

Fwpm tj eojmc

Uvp gp uihjt, uvp gp eojn

109 Initial Confusion

The initials of five **well-known proverbs** are given below. By using your word skills and general knowledge, can you restore all of the original proverbs?

YCTAHTWBYCMHD

WSFTGISFTG

WGUMCD

GCWCID

BITTW

SOLUTIONS

1.

You'll need to make at least 11 journeys back and forth from the reception to the briefing room. One method is:

- Bring in one minister and one spy
- Take back out the minister
- Bring in two spies
- Take back out one spy
- Bring in two ministers
- Take back out one spy and one minister
- Bring in two ministers
- Take back out one spy
- Bring in two spies
- Take back out one spy
- Bring back in two spies

2.

PAPAL NUNCIO
ARCHBISHOP
REVEREND
MINISTER
PASTOR
CANON

3.

Decode the first sentence by replacing A with G, B with H, C with I and so on through to replacing Y with E and Z with F, to reveal:
If you are reading this, then you've successfully decoded it

Decode the second sentence by replacing A with M, B with N, C with O and so on through to replacing Y with K and Z with L. to reveal:
Knowledge is power, and information is liberation

Decode the third sentence by replacing A with B, B with C, C with D and so on through to replacing Y with Z and Z with A to reveal:
A Caesar cipher has been applied to this text

4.

DOWNHILL
GOGGLES
POWDER
FREESTYLE
PISTE

5.

The Catcher in the Rye by J D Salinger
A Tale of Two Cities by Charles Dickens
Alice's Adventures in Wonderland by Lewis Carroll
The Da Vinci Code by Dan Brown
The Adventures of Sherlock Holmes by Arthur Conan Doyle

6.

SCIENCE FICTION
HISTORICAL
ADVENTURE
DETECTIVE
FILM NOIR

7.

- COCK: PEACOCK and COCKEYED
- BEES: BUMBLEBEES and BEESWAX
- FORCE: REINFORCE and FORCEFULLY
- WEIGH: OUTWEIGH and WEIGHTIER
- SANDS: QUICKSANDS and SANDSTONE
- WIND: HEADWIND and WINDFALLS

SOLUTIONS

8.
Decode by replacing A with H, B with I, C with J and so on through to replacing Y with F and Z with G.
DUCKLING
LEVERET
KITTEN
PIGLET
CHICK

9.
BACKSWING
FLAT BALL
HANDICAP
KINGPIN
BOARDS
FRAME

10.
123 + 302 = 425

11.
LADY OF THE LAKE
QUEEN GUINEVERE
BLACK KNIGHT
KING ARTHUR
LANCELOT
MORDRED

12.
The prisoner at the back should count how many yellow caps are in front of him. If there are an odd number, he calls out 'yellow', whereas if there are an even number he calls out 'green'. He may or may not be correct about his own cap, and so he may or may not receive the additional sentence, but armed with this information *every one* of the other prisoners can give the correct answer.

The prisoner in front of him already knows if there are an odd or even number of yellow caps in front of him, and he now knows whether the prisoner behind him could see an odd or even number too. If he and the prisoner behind him *agree* on whether there are an even number of yellow caps then he *knows for certain* that he is wearing a green cap – if he wasn't, he would see odd when the prisoner behind saw even, and vice-versa. If, on the other hand, he *disagrees* then he must be wearing a yellow cap – it's his own cap which is changing the count.

He can then be sure to call out 'green' or 'yellow' correctly, and all the prisoners in front have to do is each time they hear a 'yellow' they should change their expectation of the number of yellow caps in front from odd to even, or from even to odd. They then apply the same logic as the previous prisoner when working out which cap they have on themselves.

13.
THE HUNCHBACK OF NOTRE DAME
THE PRINCESS AND THE FROG
BEAUTY AND THE BEAST
LADY AND THE TRAMP
LILO AND STITCH
PETER PAN

14.
Reverse the letters in each word to reveal:

- Laugh and the world laughs with you

SOLUTIONS

- The proof of the pudding is in the eating
- Two wrongs don't make a right

15.
PRINTER
LAPTOP
SCANNER
TABLET
CAMERA

16.
The Hobbit by J R R Tolkein
Harry Potter and the Chamber of Secrets by J K Rowling
The Lion, the Witch and the Wardrobe by C S Lewis
Black Beauty by Anna Sewell
Charlotte's Web by E B White

17.
FORECASTLE
PROPELLER
SPINNAKER
MAINSAIL
PORTHOLE

18.
- CLOTHES: BEDCLOTHES and CLOTHESLINE
- STOCK: LIVESTOCK and STOCKPILED
- MAR: GRAMMAR and MARRED
- THROUGH: BREAKTHROUGH and THROUGHOUT
- TURNS: DOWNTURNS and TURNSTILE
- TAP: WIRETAP and TAPPING

19.
Decode by replacing A with K, B with L, C with M and so on through to replacing Y with I and Z with J.

TASMANIAN DEVIL
TREE KANGAROO
ROCK WALLABY
BANDICOOT
WOMBAT

20.
SERENADE
VOCALIZE
INCANT
WARBLE
YODEL
ARIA

21.
1976 + 8947 = 10923

22.
MOTORCYCLE LEAP
SWORD FIGHT
ROPE SWING
BASE JUMP
CAR CHASE
SKYDIVE

23.
The couples already know each other, so have already met each other, and therefore won't hand one another identity cards. This means the maximum number of cards that a person can receive is eight – one from every other person, other than their partner. We already know that the host spy and the four couples all have different numbers of cards, but there are ten people and only nine options (zero to eight cards) which means that the host's partner must receive the same number of cards as one of the other people. The person who exchanged eight cards must be in a couple with

SOLUTIONS

the person who exchanged zero cards, otherwise they couldn't have exchanged more than seven cards. Similarly, the person who exchanged seven cards must be in a couple with the person who exchanged one card. Using similar logic, the other two arriving couples exchanged six and two cards, and five and three cards. This leaves the total of four cards, which must have been the number that the host received.

24.

BATTLEMENTS
LOOKOUT TOWER
DRAWBRIDGE
PORTCULLIS
GATEHOUSE
DUNGEON

25.

Swap consecutive pairs of letters, to reveal:

- Where there's muck there's brass
- Home is where the heart is
- The devil is in the details

26.

AUSTRALIA
MEXICO
RUSSIA
BRAZIL
CANADA

27.

The Lord of the Rings: The Return of the King
Star Wars: Episode V - The Empire Strikes Back
One Flew Over the Cuckoo's Nest
Dr. Strangelove or: How I Learned to Stop Worrying and Love the Bomb
Eternal Sunshine of the Spotless Mind

28.

ROCK AND ROLL
LAMBETH WALK
BOSSA NOVA
CHARLESTON
PASO DOBLE

29.

- LOOK: OUTLOOK and LOOKALIKE
- PAPER: SANDPAPER and PAPERWEIGHT
- POINT: GUNPOINT and POINTLESS
- SURF: WINDSURF and SURFBOARD
- CROW: SCARECROW and CROWBARS
- SHAKE: HANDSHAKE and SHAKEDOWN

30.

Decode by replacing A with I, B with J, C with K and so on through to replacing Y with G and Z with H.
DAFFODIL
EGGSHELL
MAGNOLIA
PRIMROSE
MUSTARD

31.

GRAND UNIFIED THEORY
CENTRIFUGAL FORCE
QUANTUM MECHANICS
POTENTIAL ENERGY
CHAIN REACTION
THERMODYNAMICS

SOLUTIONS

32.
69321 + 4785 = 74106

33.
BELAY DEVICE
CARABINER
DESCENDER
HARNESS
HELMET
PITONS

34.
The spy should switch doors. At the start of the game each door has a one in three chance of winning, but when the host opens a door *that he <u>knows</u> is not the winning door* then he effectively changes the choice to become 'either your original door, *or* both of these doors together'. This means that the spy has a two in three chance of winning if they switch doors, but remains with their original one in three chance of winning if they don't change their guess.

35.
MRS HUDSON
IRENE ADLER
LESTRADE
MORIARTY
WATSON
MARY

36.
Take the first letters of each word to reveal:

- Crime doesn't pay
- Blood will tell
- Money is power

37.
TRUMPETER
VIOLINIST
DRUMMER
CONDUCTOR
SOPRANO

38.
All's Well That Ends Well
As You Like It
Love's Labour's Lost
Two Gentlemen of Verona
Midsummer Night's Dream

39.
DISTRIBUTION
CONSUMPTION
COLLATERAL
EMPLOYMENT
INVESTMENT

40.

- FIRM: CONFIRM and FIRMWARE
- BURDEN: OVERBURDEN and BURDENSOME
- NUTS: CHESTNUTS and NUTSHELLS
- TIC: HERETIC and TICKING
- SIGN: COUNTERSIGN and SIGNPOSTING
- HANDLE: MANHANDLE and HANDLEBAR

41.
Decode by replacing A with Y, B with Z, C with A and so on through to replacing Y with W and Z with X.
TRANSYLVANIA
HOLY WATER
GARLIC
MIRRORS
SILVER

SOLUTIONS

42.

HEADMASTER
ASSISTANT
PRINCIPAL
PROFESSOR
LECTURER
TUTOR

43.

356247 + 381924 = 738171

44.

HELICOPTER
AQUAPLANE
TURBOPROP
JUMBO JET
ZEPPELIN
GLIDER

45.

Spies A to E must all be lying, because for any of these statements to be true then there would have to be at least two spies speaking truthfully – but none of the spies agree, so this can't be correct.

Similarly, spy G can't be telling the truth because if they were then their truth would be that they *themselves* are lying, which is a contradiction,

Meanwhile, spy F *can't* be lying because if they were then they would *all* be lying (since we already know spies A to E and G are lying), which is impossible because this would mean spy G is telling the truth, which we already know to be impossible.

This means that spy F is telling the truth, but all the rest are lying.

46.

THE GOOD THE BAD AND THE UGLY
RAIDERS OF THE LOST ARK
THE USUAL SUSPECTS
LIFE IS BEAUTIFUL
APOCALYPSE NOW
MEMENTO

47.

Convert the numbers into positions in the alphabet, so 1=A, 2=B, and so on through until 26=Z, to reveal:

- Beauty is in the eye of the beholder
- All that glitters is not gold
- Give credit where credit is due

48.

BACKHAND
ADVANTAGE
DOUBLES
SERVICE
UMPIRE

49.

David Copperfield
The Old Curiosity Shop
Nicholas Nickleby
Oliver Twist
The Pickwick Papers

50.

PEANUT BUTTER
HORSERADISH
MINT JELLY
MARMALADE
CONSERVE

51.

- UPS: MAKEUPS and UPSHOT
- HOLD: HOUSEHOLD and HOLDOVER

SOLUTIONS

- OWNERS: HOMEOWNERS and OWNERSHIP
- WINGS: VIEWINGS and WINGSPANS
- YARDS: FARMYARDS and YARDSTICKS
- DIVE: NOSEDIVE and DIVESTING

52.

Decode by replacing A with X, B with Y, C with Z and so on through to replacing Y with V and Z with W.

BLUETOOTH CARD
HARD DRIVE
SOUND CARD
HEAT SINK
PROCESSOR

53.

GRAVITY MANIPULATION
TELESCOPIC VISION
INVULNERABILITY
SUPER STRENGTH
INVISIBILITY
WEB SLINGING

54.

8972+382+1072=10426

55.

SHIPWRECK
BARNACLE
SEAHORSE
DOLPHIN
OCTOPUS
CORAL

56.

- Jimmy Blond used Quantum Listening technology in the CIA Headquarters by using the Vocalitass
- James Welsh used Latent Observation methods when he used the Craniator in Bletchley Park.
- Richard Cord made use of Inverse Phasing at the UK Parliament when he used his Interceptorion.
- Karen Ambler used the Netterbot at The White House, taking advantage of Viral Attachment technology.

57.

PERSEUS
ROBIN HOOD
GILGAMESH
ACHILLES
LANCELOT
MEDUSA

58.

Take the last letter of each word to reveal:

- Talk is cheap
- Time will tell
- Truth will out

59.

ELEPHANT
GORILLA
PORCUPINE
WHALE
SQUIRREL

60.

All You Need Is Love
Can't Buy Me Love
A Hard Day's Night
Hey Jude
I Want to Hold Your Hand

SOLUTIONS

61.
BLACKSMITH
GUNSLINGER
HIGH NOON
SADDLEBAG
TOMBSTONE

62.
- HARD: DIEHARD and HARDBACK
- FRIENDS: GIRLFRIENDS and FRIENDSHIP
- PHONE: EARPHONE and PHONETIC
- ANY: LITANY and ANYHOW
- PAN: BEDPAN and PANHANDLERS
- OFFS: LIFTOFFS and OFFSHOOTS

63.
Decode by replacing A with D, B with E, C with F and so on through to replacing Y with B and Z with C.
PILE DRIVER
BULLDOZER
EXCAVATOR
BACKHOE
GRADER

64.
DONKEY KONG JUNIOR
MISSILE COMMAND
SPACE INVADERS
POLE POSITION
ASTEROIDS
CENTIPEDE

65.
4037 – 786 – 2316 = 935

66.
DOPPELGANGER
KINDERGARTEN
FRANKFURTER
POLTERGEIST
WANDERLUST
STRUDEL

67.
The spy draws one of the pieces of paper out of the box but before it can be viewed he puts it in his mouth and swallows it. He hopes that the host will then remove the other piece of paper, which will say 'LOSE', and assume that he drew the 'WIN' paper.

68.
AIRCRAFT CARRIER
SUPERTANKER
MINESWEEPER
PADDLE STEAMER
LIFEBOAT
DREDGER

69.
The numbers are binary values, which index letters into the alphabet, with 00001=A through to 11010=Z. If you convert first to decimal you have 1=A, 2=B, and so on through until 26=Z. The proverbs are:
- Every cloud has a silver lining
- Better safe than sorry
- More haste, less speed

SOLUTIONS

70.
CHAINSAW
HAMMER
PLANE
SCREWDRIVER
WRENCH

71.
Colin Firth for *The King's Speech*
Eddie Redmayne for *The Theory of Everything*
Leonardo DiCaprio for *The Revenant*
Kevin Spacey for *American Beauty*
Tom Hanks for *Forrest Gump*

72.
OUT OF BOUNDS
FREE THROW
POSSESSION
BACKBOARD
BACKCOURT

73.
- EAST: SOUTHEAST and EASTWARD
- DAD: GRANDDAD and DADDIES
- CUR: CONCUR and CURABLE
- MISS: DISMISS and MISSION
- CHARGE: OVERCHARGE and CHARGEABLE
- PRINT: FINGERPRINT and PRINTOUT

74.
Decode by replacing A with L, B with M, C with N and so on through to replacing Y with J and Z with K.
- MEDITERRANEAN
- HIGH-PROTEIN
- GLUTEN-FREE
- PALEOLITHIC
- PESCATARIAN

75.
OYSTERCATCHER
SHEARWATER
ALBATROSS
CORMORANT
GUILLEMOT
PENGUIN

76.
744 + 150 + 692 = 1586

77.
DODECAHEDRON
CYLINDER
PYRAMID
CUBOID
SPHERE
TORUS

78.
The spy takes a piece of ammunition from the box marked 'mixed pistol and rifle ammunition'. They know that the box has the wrong label on it, so if they draw an item of pistol ammunition they know this must be the 'pistol' box, not the 'mixed' box. Because all the labels are wrong, they then know that the 'rifle' box must contain the mixed ammunition, since it can't contain the rifle ammunition and they have already found the pistol ammunition. This then means that the box with the 'pistol' label must contain the rifle ammunition, and they have identified all three boxes.

If they draw an item of rifle ammunition then they know they have found the rifle box, and the box with the 'pistol' label must be the mixed box. This would then mean that the box with the 'rifle' label must be the pistol box.

79.
MULLED WINE
CAPPUCCINO
ESPRESSO
AMERICANO
EGGNOG
SAKE

80.
These are Vigenère ciphers, meaning that each letter has a Caesar cipher applied but that the cipher shift varies from letter to letter. The word before each phrase is the cipher codeword, revealing how to shift each letter. The first letter of the codeword shows the shift applied to the first letter; the second letter of the codeword shows the shift applied to the second letter; and so on. Once you pass the last letter of the codeword you start again from the first letter.

Each shift is given as the letter that an 'A' becomes, so if the first letter of the codeword is a 'D' then for the first letter of the encoded information you should convert a D to an A, an E to a B, and so on. If the second letter is 'O', then for the second letter of the encoded information you convert an O to an A, a P to B, and so on.

Once you have decoded each proverb with that line's given codeword you will have:
- Let the buyer beware
- It is better to give than to receive
- What you don't know can't hurt you

81.
SWIMMING
BADMINTON
VOLLEYBALL
GYMNASTICS
ARCHERY

82.
Emma Stone for *La La Land*
Julianne Moore for *Still Alice*
Jennifer Lawrence for *Silver Linings Playbook*
Natalie Portman for *Black Swan*
Kate Winslet for *The Reader*

83.
ORCHESTRA PIT
STAGE MANAGER
CURTAIN CALL
STAGE FRIGHT
FIRST NIGHT

84.
- COME: OUTCOME and COMEDIES
- PIT: COCKPIT and PITTING
- TURN: DOWNTURN and TURNOUT
- WEIGHT: LIGHTWEIGHT and WEIGHTLESS
- FORTH: HENCEFORTH and FORTHWITH
- BEAR: OVERBEAR and BEARABLE

85.
Decode by replacing A with F, B with G, C with H and so on through to replacing Y with D and Z with E.
- PROMETHEUS

SOLUTIONS

- HYPERION
- CALYPSO
- IAPETUS
- TITAN

86.
MARS PATHFINDER
LUNAR ORBITER
SPACE SHUTTLE
MESSENGER
GALILEO
SPUTNIK

87.
135 × 548 = 73980

88.
EN GARDE
RIPOSTE
ATTACK
POMMEL
FEINT
LUNGE

89.
- For the first challenge, the spy asked one of the henchmen, 'Which of you would the other one say tells the truth?'. Whichever henchmen was given as the answer was the one who always lied, and the other one was the one who always told the truth.

  This works because if the spy asked the truth-teller then they will answer with what the other henchman will say, so they will tell a lie. If, on the other hand, they ask the liar then they know that the other henchman would tell the truth so they lie. In both cases, the answer results in the henchman who is the liar.

- The liar can't say 'I always lie' because this would be true, and therefore a contradiction. The truth-teller can't say 'I always lie' because this would be a lie and they only tell the truth. So the henchman saying 'I always lie' must be the third henchman who can both lie and tell the truth as he pleases.

90.
SYNCHRONIZED DIVING
BODYBOARDING
KITESURFING
WATER POLO
KAYAKING
FISHING

91.
The numbers are hexadecimal (base 16) values which index into letters into the alphabet, where 01=A, 02=B,..., 08=H, 09=I, 0A=J, 0B=K,..., 0F=O, 10=P, 11=Q through to 1A=Z. If you convert first to decimal you have 1=A, 2=B, and so on through until 26=Z. The proverbs are:
- The devil is in the details
- Charity begins at home
- You're never too old to learn

92.
GEORGIA
MICHIGAN
OREGON
VIRGINIA
ALABAMA

SOLUTIONS

93.

The Phantom of the Opera
Beauty and the Beast
The Book of Mormon
Fiddler on the Roof
The Lion King

94.

CAPTAIN AMERICA
INVISIBLE WOMAN
GREEN LANTERN
MR FANTASTIC
WONDER WOMAN

95.

- ROOM: BATHROOM and ROOMMATES
- HIP: INTERNSHIP and HIPPIES
- PUN: HOMESPUN and PUNTING
- TIN: MARTIN and TINFOIL
- SELF: ONESELF and SELFLESS
- GRASS: BLUEGRASS and GRASSLAND

96.

Decode by replacing A with Y, B with Z, C with A and so on through to replacing Y with W and Z with X.

- BRACQUEMOND
- PISSARRO
- CEZANNE
- RENOIR
- MONET

97.

CHAISE LONGUE
EJECTOR
OTTOMAN
SADDLE
BENCH
DIVAN

98.

1589 × 1571 = 2496319

99.

NECKERCHIEF
BOW TIE
MUFFLER
CRAVAT
SCARF
STOLE

100.

- CARD: POSTCARD and CARDBOARD
- PAY: UNDERPAY and PAYLOAD
- MAIL: AIRMAIL and MAILMEN
- SWORD: PASSWORD and SWORDFISHES
- FIELD: MINEFIELD and FIELDWORK
- TABLE: TIMETABLE and TABLECLOTH

101.

NEWFOUNDLAND
GREAT BRITAIN
MADAGASCAR
SUMATRA
NEW GUINEA
CUBA

102.

PHOSPHORUS
BERYLLIUM
GERMANIUM
MAGNESIUM
MANGANESE

103.

SHOT ACROSS THE BOWS
FLASHING LIGHT
POLICE WHISTLE
STORM WARNING

SOLUTIONS

CAR HORN
RED FLAG

104.
Decode by replacing A with S, B with T, C with U and so on through to replacing Y with Q and Z with R.
- MULTIPLICATION
- ARITHMETIC
- LOGARITHM
- NUMERATOR
- EQUATION

105.
FABRIC SOFTENER
WASHING POWDER
DRY CLEANING
TUMBLE DRIER
DRYING RACK
STEAM IRON

106.
- GAL: FUNGAL and GALLOPED
- LEADERS: RINGLEADERS and LEADERSHIP
- LENGTH: WAVELENGTH and LENGTHWISE
- CUT: SHORTCUT and CUTTINGS
- COAT: TURNCOAT and COATROOM
- WIRE: HAYWIRE and WIRETAPPING

107.
91254 + 1837 = 93091

108.
Reverse each word and then apply a Caesar shift of one letter backwards, changing A to Z, B to A and so on to reveal:
- No good deed goes unpunished
- Love is blind
- Out of sight, out of mind

109.
You can take a horse to water but you can't make him drink
What's sauce for the goose is sauce for the gander
What goes up must come down
Give credit where credit is due
Blood is thicker than water